DRAGON RESURRECTION™
The First Adventure of Jesse and Jack Chang

STORY
Lin Zhang & Lyan Zhang

SCRIPT
Mark Byers

COVER
Vosa Wang

FOR DEZERLIN MEDIA

ART
Erfan Fajar

CHARACTER DESIGNS
Erfan Fajar & Bagus Hutomo

COLORS
Sakti Yuwono, Beny Maulana & Yenny Laud

BACK COVER
Bagus Hutomo

FOR IMAGINARY FRIENDS STUDIOS

LETTERING
Blambot®'s Nate Piekos

DARK HORSE BOOKS

PUBLISHER
Mike Richardson

DIGITAL PRODUCTION
Ryan Jorgensen

DESIGNER
Adam Grano

EDITOR
Brendan Wright

Special thanks to JianChang Zhang, encourager; Song Yi Chun, inspiration; and Ling Yan and Teuku Muharram, project managers.

DRAGON RESURRECTION™: THE FIRST ADVENTURE OF JESSE AND JACK CHANG
© 2013, 2014 DeZerlin Media. All rights reserved. Dark Horse Books® and the Dark Horse logo are registered trademarks of Dark Horse Comics, Inc. All rights reserved. No portion of this publication may be reproduced or transmitted, in any form or by any means, without the express written permission of Dark Horse Comics, Inc. Names, characters, places, and incidents featured in this publication either are the product of the author's imagination or are used fictitiously. Any resemblance to actual persons (living or dead), events, institutions, or locales, without satiric intent, is coincidental.

Published by Dark Horse Books
A division of Dark Horse Comics, Inc.
10956 SE Main Street
Milwaukie, OR 97222

DarkHorse.com
DeZerlin.com

International Licensing: (503) 905-2377
To find a comics shop in your area, call the Comic Shop Locator Service toll-free at (888) 266-4226.

Scholastic edition: January 2014
ISBN 978-1-61655-404-0

Library of Congress Cataloging-in-Publication Data

Dragon resurrection : the first adventure of Jesse and Jack Chang / story, Lin Zhang & Lyan Zhang ; script, Mark Byers ; cover, Vosa Wang ; art, Erfan Fajar ; character designs, Erfan Fajar & Bagus Hutomo ; colors, Sakti Yuwono, Beny Maulana, & Yenny Laud ; back cover, Bagus Hutomo. — First Edition.
     pages cm
  ISBN 978-1-61655-102-5
  1. Dragons—Comic books, strips, etc. 2. Twins—Comic books, strips, etc. 3. Graphic novels. I. Zhang, Lin, 1985- creator. II. Zhang, Lyan, creator. III. Byers, Mark, 1953- author. IV. Wang, Vosa, illustrator. V. Fajar, Erfan, illustrator. VI. Hutomo, Bagus, illustrator.
  PN6790.C44D73 2013
  741.5'951—dc23
                    2013001613

10 9 8 7 6 5 4 3 2 1
Printed in China

ONCE THE QIN EMPEROR WAS ASSURED OF HIS SUPREME RULE, HE FEARED THAT THE VERY DRAGONS WHO BROUGHT HIM VICTORY MIGHT BE USED IN A COUP AGAINST HIM.

DEFYING THE COMMAND OF THE EMPEROR, GENERAL BAI QI ESCAPED ON THE LAST OF THE BLUE DRAGONS, AND GENERAL LIU FAN ESCAPED ON THE LAST RED YING DRAGON, AND DRAGONS DISAPPEARED INTO THE MISTS OF TIME, BECOMING NOTHING MORE THAN MYTHS AND LEGENDS.

UNTIL TODAY...

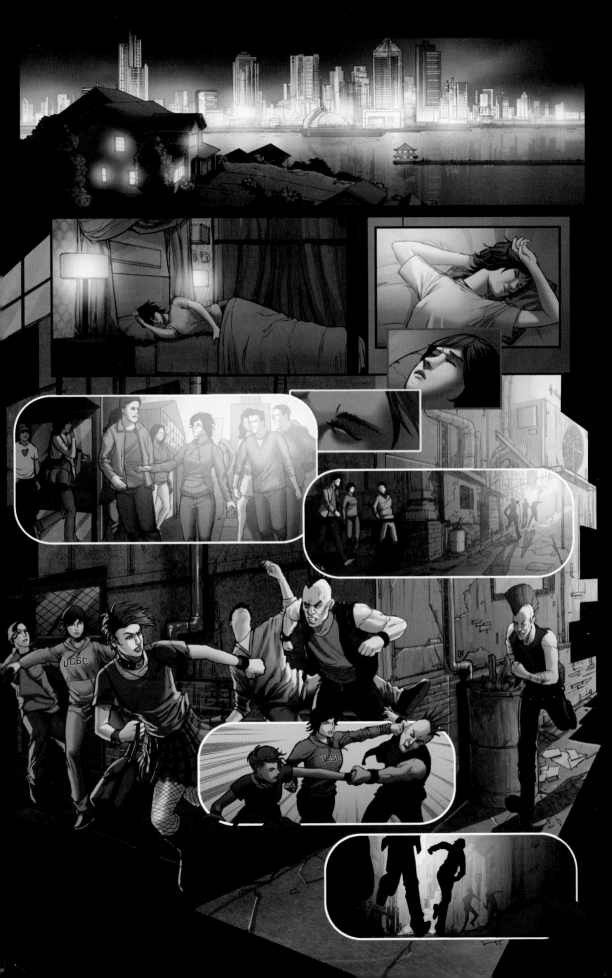

THAT BIG YELLOW BALL IN THE SKY IS CALLED THE SUN...
I'VE GOT IT! I'VE FOUND THE GENETIC KEY!
SORRY, EINSTEIN--NO NOBEL PRIZE JUST YET...
JACK, YOU'VE BEEN HAMMERING AT THIS REPTILE D.N.A. FOR MONTHS NOW, AND IT'S JUST NOT GETTING US ANYWHERE.
YOU WERE MAKING REAL PROGRESS WITH THE RHINOCEROS BEETLE. I WANT YOU TO GET BACK TO THAT...
JACK-- WE'RE NOT SUPPOSED TO BE WORKING ON THIS ANYMORE. QUE COULD SEND US BACK TO BEING TEACHING ASSISTANTS...
I KNOW I CAN DO THIS! WE'RE SO CLOSE. PLEASE, KATE-- HELP ME WITH THIS.
I CAN'T SAY NO TO YOU, JACK...
YOU WERE RIGHT. TELLING HIM TO STOP JUST REDOUBLED HIS EFFORTS. HE SHOULD HAVE A BREAKTHROUGH SOON.

"JESSE'S BOYFRIEND DIED. I GUESS I WAS *LUCKY*--ONLY *HALF* OF ME DIED."

"BUT IT WAS *WORST* FOR JESSE. HER INJURIES WERE JUST A *BROKEN ARM*, A COUPLE OF *CRACKED RIBS*, BUT SHE *BLAMED HERSELF* FOR EVERYTHING..."

...ESPECIALLY FOR WHAT HAPPENED TO *YOU*. SURVIVOR'S GUILT.

IT *WASN'T* HER FAULT! AND IF I CAN JUST *WALK* AGAIN...

JACK *NEVER* TAKES TIME OFF. WHERE'S *MY BROTHER,* KATE?

I DON'T *KNOW,* BUT I'LL *FIND* HIM.

YOU'LL FIND HIM? SHOULDN'T WE GO TO THE *POLICE?*

THE POLICE CAN'T HELP US. I NEED YOU TO *TRUST ME,* JESSE.

TRUST YOU? BEFORE *TODAY,* ALL YOU WERE WAS AN *IMAGE* ON VIDEO CHAT!

WHERE *ARE* WE?

DIDN'T HE SEND YOU PICTURES? THIS IS JACK'S PLACE.

LOOK, JESSE, I HAVE NO PROOF, BUT ALL THE EVIDENCE POINTS TO D.A.R.P.A.*--THE BRANCH OF THE DEPARTMENT OF DEFENSE THAT DEVELOPS NEW TECHNOLOGY FOR THE MILITARY.

I BELIEVE JACK'S RESEARCH MADE HIM A TARGET OF THEIR GENETIC RESEARCH AND APPLICATIONS DIVISION.

*THE DEFENSE ADVANCED RESEARCH PROJECTS AGENCY

WAIT--IF YOU'RE JUST A RESEARCH ASSISTANT, HOW COULD YOU POSSIBLY KNOW ALL OF THIS?

YOU ARE SO NAIVE. ASK ANYONE WHO WORKS IN THE SCIENCE DEPARTMENT OF ANY MAJOR UNIVERSITY-- MILITARY EYES ARE ALWAYS CAREFULLY WATCHING THE ADVANCED RESEARCH PROJECTS.

SO WHERE IS MY BROTHER?

I'VE GOT PEOPLE WORKING ON THAT...

54° 26' South, 3° 24' East / Z + 150 Kilometers / D.A.R.P.A.
Genetic Research and Applications Division Research Laboratory

33° 55' South 18° 25' East
Cape Town, South Africa.

"KATE, HOW DOES A *RESEARCH ASSISTANT* JUST DRIVE ONTO A *MILITARY BASE* LIKE THIS? WHAT *ARE* YOU, SOME KIND OF *SECRET AGENT...?*"

"*CENTRAL INTELLIGENCE AGENCY.* I'M *SURE* YOU'VE *HEARD* OF US."

"I WAS *KIDDING.*"

"*I'M* NOT. I'M WHAT WE CALL A *SCI-SPY*—A SCIENCE SPY, TASKED WITH *PROTECTING* PROMISING SCIENTISTS AND RESEARCH, TO KEEP IT FROM FALLING INTO THE *WRONG HANDS.*"

BECAUSE I HOLD A GRADUATE DEGREE IN GENETIC ENGINEERING, I WAS *ASSIGNED* TO WATCH OVER YOUR BROTHER.

DR. QUE IS A RECRUITER FOR THE DEPARTMENT OF DEFENSE, AND HE GOT ME IN. BUT WE FOUND OUT HE WAS TAKING *MONEY* TO PASS ALONG *INFORMATION* ABOUT PROMISING GENETIC RESEARCH.

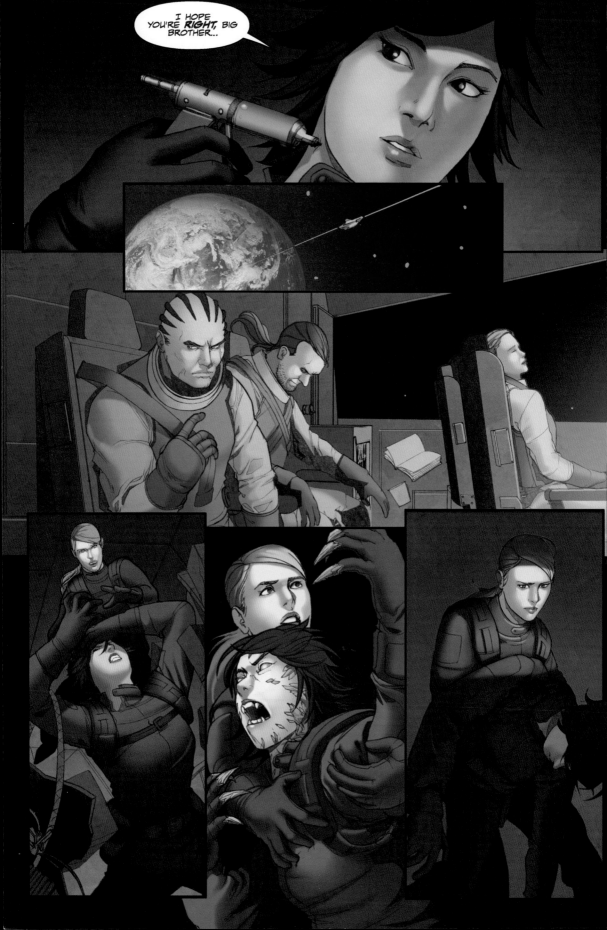

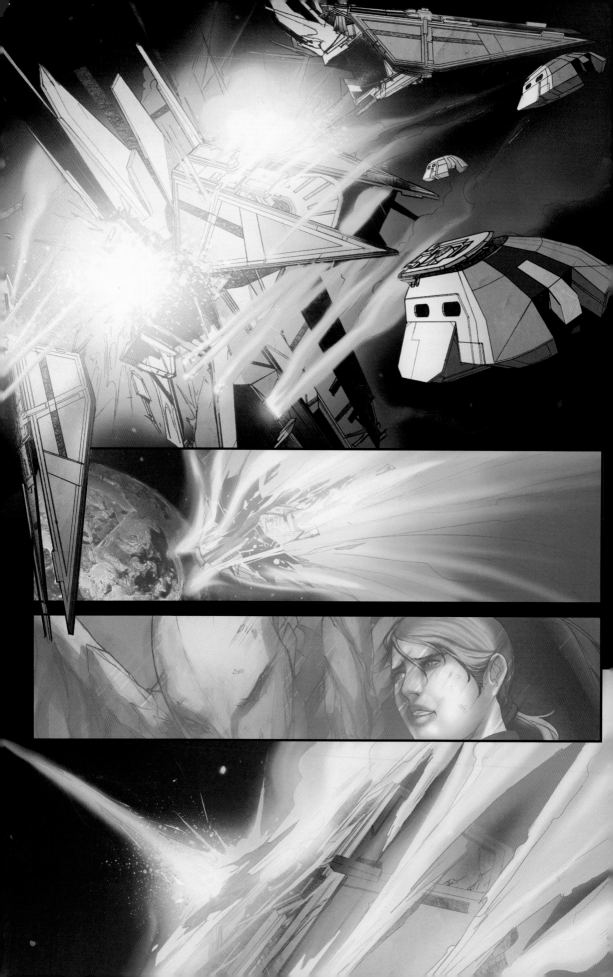

I MEAN NO DISRESPECT.

THIS... THIS IS AN ANCIENT *CHINESE CHARACTER*. IT MEANS... *DRAGON*...

MKUDA CHITSANDUKWA!

MKUDA CHITSANDUKWA!

MKUDA CHITSANDUKWA!

MKUDA CHITSANDUKWA!

NO ONE HAS REALLY *STUDIED* THESE PEOPLE. I HAVE *NO IDEA* WHAT THIS CEREMONY IS ABOUT...

IT'S THE STORY OF THE COMING OF *MY PEOPLE*...

RELAX, CAJOU. I'VE BEEN EXPECTING THIS. YOU WANTED TO SHOW YOUR BUYERS A **DEMONSTRATION** OF THE PRODUCT--**THIS** IS YOUR COMMERCIAL.

COMMERCIAL?

WHAT COULD BE BETTER FOR SALES THAN A **CLASSIFIED VIDEO** LEAKED TO THE INTERNET SHOWING A U.S. MARINE UNIT BEING **WIPED OUT** BY GENETIC SUPER-SOLDIERS?

IT'LL START A BIDDING WAR WORTH **TENS** OF BILLIONS. **BRILLIANT!**

GENERAL, I'VE FOUND A GENETIC MATCH FOR THE DRAGON D.N.A.!

YOU'RE FINALLY EARNING YOUR **KEEP**, DOCTOR. GET ALL YOUR DATA ONTO PORTABLE DRIVES-- WE'RE GONNA TAKE THIS **SHOW** ON THE ROAD.

CAPTAIN ANTONELLI, TIME TO PREPARE **PHASE TWO.**

EXCELLENT, SIR. WE'RE ALL **READY.**

BE AWARE, THE *BLUE DRAGON* IS WITH THEM.

I HAD THE DOCTOR PREPARE A LITTLE *"BOOSTER"* FOR YOU. YOU GET INTO *TROUBLE* WITH THE DRAGON, SHOOT YOURSELF FULL OF *THIS*-- IT'LL INCREASE YOUR STRENGTH AND STAMINA BY A FACTOR OF TEN.

THEY'RE COMING *THROUGH!* TRANSFORM *NOW!*

THE
FORMULA!
INJECT
YOURSELF
WITH THE
FORMULA!

GOODBYE FOR NOW--I'M *CERTAIN* WE'RE GOING TO MEET AGAIN ONE DAY *SOON.*

AFTER ALL, EVERYTHING TO THIS POINT HAS JUST BEEN THE R. & D. PHASE OF A *MUCH LARGER* OPERATION...

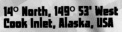

14° North, 149° 53' West
Cook Inlet, Alaska, USA

52° North, 77° 3' West
Arlington, Virginia, USA.
The Pentagon.

DOESN'T *LOOK* MUCH LIKE A PENTAGON ON THE INSIDE.

WHAT DID YOU EXPECT-- *TRIANGULAR* HALLWAYS?

MUST BE *IMPORTANT* FOR THEM TO LET TWO *CHINESE* NATIONALS INTO THIS PLACE.

THEY SAID IT WAS *URGENT,* ASKED FOR THE TWO OF YOU *SPECIFICALLY.*

OVER HERE, PLEASE!

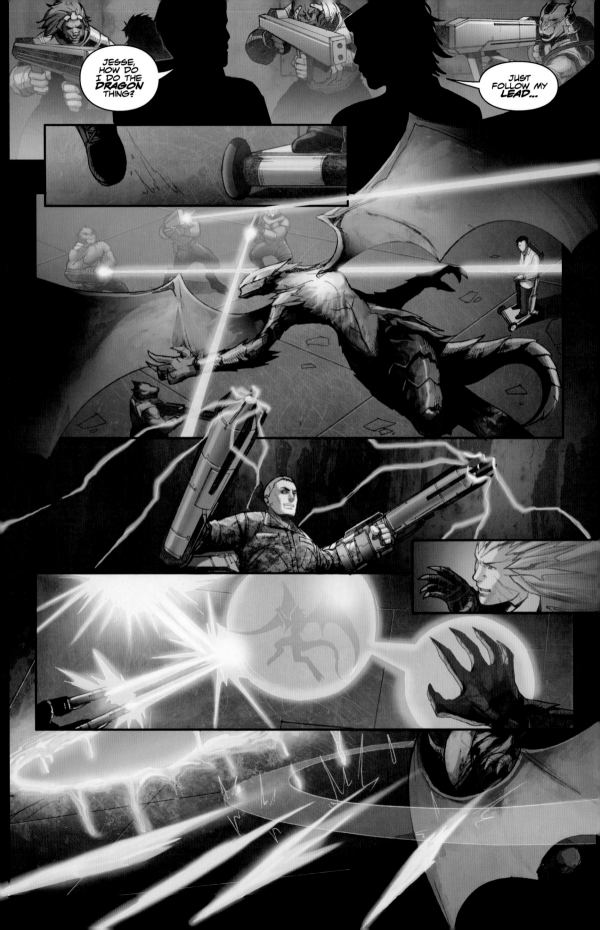

AND THEY ARE HERE
TO STAY, A GIFT FROM
CHINA FOR THE PEACE
AND SECURITY OF
THE ENTIRE WORLD.

The End

DRAGON RESURRECTION™
The Animated Motion Picture

Jesse and Jack Chang's epic battle with
General Vladimir and his fusion beasts
comes to the big screen in the fall of 2014.

DEZERLIN.COM

Mike Richardson, President and Publisher | Neil Hankerson, Executive Vice President | Tom Weddle, Chief Financial Officer | Randy Stradley, Vice President of Publishing | Michael Martens, Vice President of Book Trade Sales | Anita Nelson, Vice President of Business Affairs | Scott Allie, Editor in Chief | Matt Parkinson, Vice President of Marketing | David Scroggy, Vice President of Product Development | Dale LaFountain, Vice President of Information Technology | Darlene Vogel, Senior Director of Print, Design, and Production | Ken Lizzi, General Counsel | Davey Estrada, Editorial Director | Chris Warner, Senior Books Editor | Diana Schutz, Executive Editor | Cary Grazzini, Director of Print and Development | Lia Ribacchi, Art Director | Cara Niece, Director of Scheduling | Tim Wiesch, Director of International Licensing | Mark Bernardi, Director of Digital Publishing